THANK YOU, WORLD

Dial Books for *Young Readers*

United States

Mexico

Mali

Saudi Arabia

Bolivia

France

India

China

Thank you, swing. You shoot me like a rocket

past birds and grass and trees.

Thank you, trees. Your branches are my playhouse.

I'm climbing to the clouds!

Thank you, clouds, for painting cotton pictures

and sending cool, sweet rain.

Thank you, window. You welcome in the moonlight

that yawns from starry skies.

Thank you, stars, for sparkling so brightly.

You shine like Mommy's eyes.

Thank you, Mommy, for tucking in my tiptoes

and kissing me good night.

United States.

Mexico

Mali

Saudi Arabia

Bolivia

France

India

China